TRINITY
COLLEGE LONDON PRESS

CW00376632

GRADE

01
PIANO

Pieces & Exercises for
Trinity College London
Exams 2018-2020

Includes CD &
teaching notes

Published by
Trinity College London Press
trinitycollege.com

Registered in England
Company no. 09726123

Printed in England by Halstan & Co Ltd., Amersham, Bucks.

Mango Walk

(duet part)

Barbara Kirkby-Mason
(1910–2000)

Mango Walk

(candidate's part)

Barbara Kirkby-Mason
(1910–2000)

Allemande

Arr. Snell

Johann Hermann Schein
(1586-1630)

Do not play the repeats in the exam.

Minuet

No. 10 from *24 Short and Easy Pieces*

Alexander Reinagle
(1756–1804)

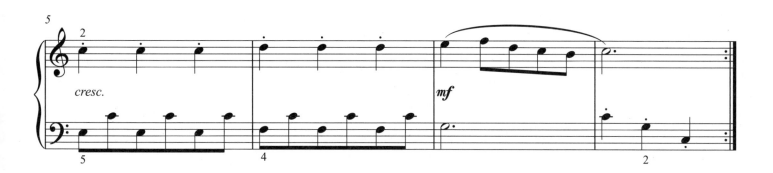

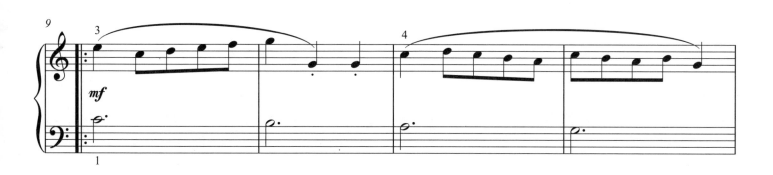

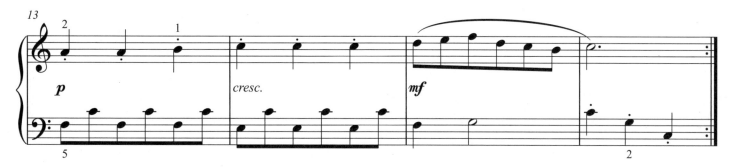

Do not play the repeats in the exam.

I'm Happy

Joyce Grill
(b. 1936)

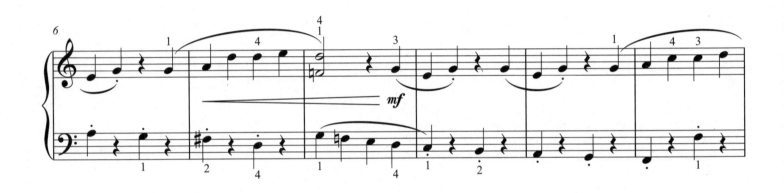

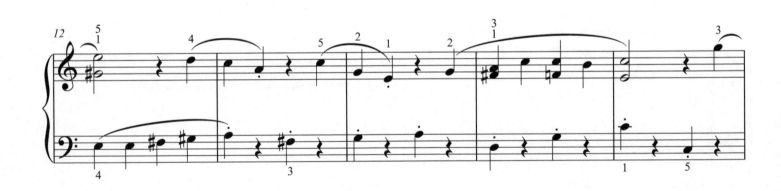

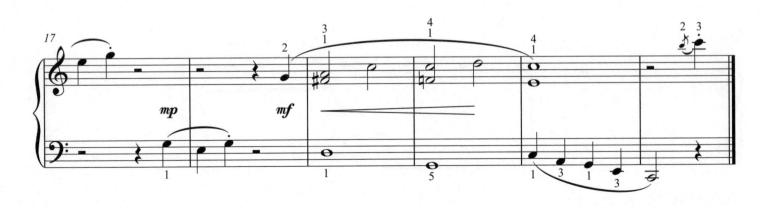

6

Just for Starters

Mike Mower
(b. 1958)

The Enchanted Garden

Kirsten Strecke
(b. 1961)

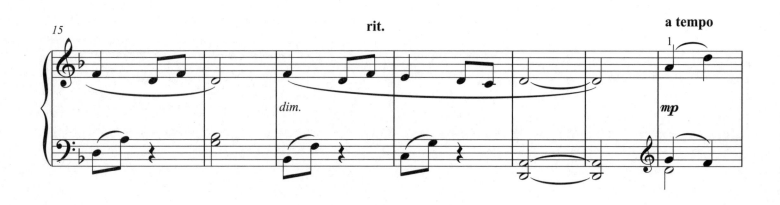

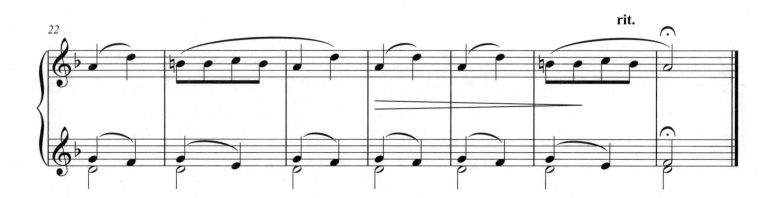

Walking (and Talking)

Kay Charlton
(b. 1963)

Jodler

(Yodeler)

Uli Gruber
(b. 1964)

Hand in Hand

Ben Crosland
(b. 1968)

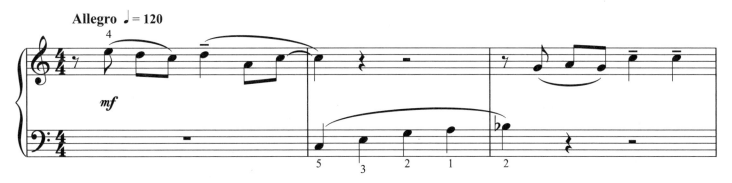

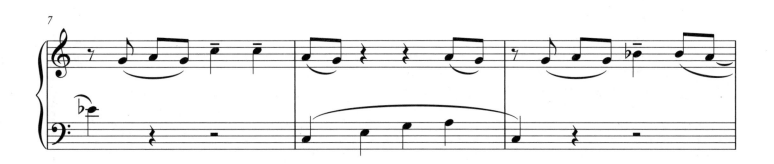

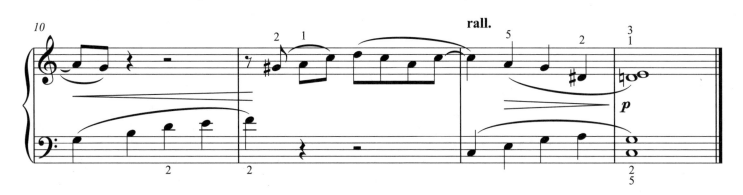

© 2009 Spartan Press Music Publishers Limited, Unit 2B Station Road, Kingussie, Highland PH21 1ER

Exercises

1a. Tundra – tone, balance and voicing

1b. A Minor Blues – tone, balance and voicing

2a. Pas de Deux – co-ordination

2b. The Ming Vase – co-ordination

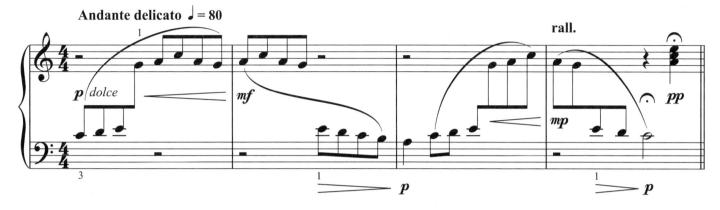

3a. Going Underground – finger & wrist strength and flexibility

3b. Capriccio – finger & wrist strength and flexibility

Teaching notes

Kirkby-Mason Mango Walk (duet) page 2

I can imagine that this will be a popular duet, with many pianists already knowing the catchy tune. I would take the opportunity to discuss chords I and V⁷, whose broken chords feature in several bars, either divided between the hands or hands together. Find the tonic triad and then its inversions, stopping on the second inversion. If you then play the first bar of the melody, can your student find the notes and rhythm for bar 2 using just the inversion of the triad? If they can work out the notes themselves, first RH, then LH, then divided between the hands, this will make remembering what happens in bars 2, 4, 6, 8, etc so much easier. We remember what we understand. You can play a similar game with V⁷. An alternative fingering for the beginning would be 3 on the D, using 1, 4 on the B, C on the sixth & seventh quavers.

A note about the pauses: one of the players will need to lead the release of these chords, and you could try it both ways. But the mood is upbeat, fun, so the pause doesn't want to be so long that it fades into *p*, but rather wants to release with energy, almost with a flourish at the end. So time the pause so that the drive of the *crescendo* takes you all the way into the rest. It's tricky to synchronise the last bar with the arpeggiated chord in secondo, so a little easing into the bar may help here. Finally, smile before you begin; this is one that should have examiners tapping their feet!

Schein *arr.* Snell Allemande page 4

My trusty but rather ancient *Concise Oxford Dictionary* writes about the Allemande: 'in character it is serious but not heavy and in speed moderate'. That just about sums up this example by Schein – somewhat stately and formal, but with the possibility of some enlivening articulation.

The phrasing in the top part has been carefully marked and observing the shaping in bars 4 & 10, with the smallest break in sound after the third crotchet, will help avoid its being too four square. The accompaniment has been left bare and it is here that some judicious lifting will preserve the Allemande's dance origins. Try making both crotchets in bar 2 articulated, light. Same again for the repeated As in bar 5, and perhaps in bar 4 too. You could use a similar strategy in bars 7 & 8 or you may prefer to keep these bars entirely *legato* as a contrast. This is beautifully crafted with its six-bar halves and use of sequence and repetition. The speed, yes, moderate, but feel that buoyancy in the mood. No need for repeats in the exam.

Reinagle Minuet (no. 10 from *24 Short and Easy Pieces*) page 5

Primary triad harmonies, with the occasional ii⁰ in place of IV, a balanced phrase structure, and a serviceable, if uninspiring, melody. Almost painting by numbers, but still pedagogically useful. The Minuet has three beats in a bar, but really just the one stress, emphasised by also having only one harmony per bar. So it is important to find an unhurried tempo but to feel one beat, one gesture per bar. Later, as Beethoven's Minuets became cheekier and faster, they would turn into Scherzos. The suggested tempo here is excellent; don't let it drag.

Much else is self-explanatory. A little rotary motion, keeping that wrist flexible, will help the LH in bars 5-6 and 13-14. Show us the difference between the two bar *crescendo* in the first of those, and the one bar *crescendo* in bar 14. Only to *mf* though – this Minuet keeps its elegance and does not need anything stronger in dynamic. Is anyone else reminded of another Minuet in bar 9 – perhaps Reinagle paying homage to Bach/Petzold?

Grill I'm Happy page 6

There's a lot of moving around the keyboard in this piece, so it will probably suit someone comfortable with the geography of the keyboard. The small phrases and frequent rests cleverly allow plenty of time to move to new positions. Try to encourage pianists to think about where they are going *before* changing position. Distances are usually pretty small, quite often entailing just a change of finger on the same note. Think first, then move – it always reminds me of the 'mirror, signal, manoeuvre' I was taught at driving school!

Some repeated notes come under a slur, as in bar 7 or 11 and, although a real *legato* is not possible, aim to make these long and melodic. Check too that the lower notes in the small chords in bars 15 and 19-20 release and don't linger under the next single notes. The *mp/mf* contrast is cleverly enhanced by moving the LH down an octave at bar 9. The double basses have clearly joined in at this point, adding extra sonority, to which the RH must respond. Enjoy the *crescendo* at the end, keeping a good *f* in the bass, down to the bottom C, then cutting everything off with a cheeky *acciaccatura*.

Mower Just for Starters page 7

Mike Mower's piece is quite ingenious, and makes me smile every time I play it. There's also something quite sophisticated about the modulations and it reminds me of the way Beethoven can suddenly make a turn into a completely alien key, often as a joke, wrong-footing the listener, but easily finding his way back home.

We begin innocently enough with a C major triad in unison. One bar later and we are in E minor. Back to C, then G. Right, start again. This time we go through F, D minor and B♭. Wonderful! It is important for pianists to understand what is going on, both so that they can enjoy the joke, but also so that they realise they are telling a story as the music twists and turns through these different keys. Which notes are the ones that tell us we are going somewhere new? Those will be the ones to lead towards, to colour, to highlight in some way. No articulation is marked, so you could use that to point up interesting moments, for instance separating the notes in bar 8. Begin bar 9 at a lower dynamic to make the *crescendo* more effective and disappear at the end without the ceremony of a *ritardando*.

Strecke The Enchanted Garden page 8

Pedalling is not expected at this level, but we automatically want to see the garden through rose-tinted, hazy spectacles to reproduce that sense of enchantment. Stick as closely as possible to the keys, lightening the second note of the slur, but without releasing it too early. A sigh of wonderment, of suspended belief; we step gently, almost reverentially, through the gate. Release those second crotchets too quickly and the mood will become jaunty and lose its magic. Similarly, the cello needs much subtlety in shaping its fifths from bar 9, supporting the RH melody as you venture further along the path, but not disrupting its *cantabile* character.

The wrist has a large part to play here. It channels the weight of the arm to depress the initial notes, then rises in preparation for the next downbeat, playing the second note of the slur as it does so, making the second note more passive, gentler in sound. Such a useful technique to master and this is a good piece to practise it on. Listen to the pedal D, ensuring there is enough sound on it for us to hear its stability, to hear that our garden visitor is too enchanted to move for 8 bars.

Charlton Walking (and Talking) page 9

C major, a relaxed tempo, some repetition and we know how good Kay Charlton is at writing light-hearted pieces. But there is a wealth of detail here, which makes it more interesting than some choices, but demands sharp eyes and ears.

The opening material returns in bar 17 one dynamic level higher. Think added confidence, an extra saxophone added to the ensemble, a brighter colour. Imagination will add extra energy to the fingers, hopefully resulting in the higher dynamic without pushing. A good *p* in the preceding bar will also help the *f* to sound stronger. Notice that the two-note slurs are usually within a *crescendo* (as in bar 4), with the second quaver marked *staccato*, so this is not an occasion for drop-float, instead the second note needs more energy. Strangely the quavers in bar 7 are not marked in the same way, but the effect is almost identical. In bar 2, release the RH minim with the last *staccato* in the LH; to hold it on sounds pedantic. There are several places where both hands have rests, bars 4, 20, etc. Listen to make sure there really is silence and, although it may be tempting, the quavers should be played evenly and not 'swung'.

Gruber	Jodler (Yodeler)	page 10

If you play through this delightful piece, you will easily guess that Jodler means a yodel, or a yodeler. Memories of *The Sound of Music* and the 'Lonely Goatherd' perhaps! The yodels fall beautifully under the fingers, encouraging a gentle rotary motion, but always keeping the fifth finger rounded and supported. If rotary motion becomes too exaggerated you end up using the side, rather than the tip or pad of the finger. Meanwhile the LH has the challenge of putting the weight on the weaker side of the hand, fingers 5 & 4, while making sure the thumb releases with a light touch. Again, check that the LH little finger is not collapsing.

There are basically two lines of music here, each repeated at a lower dynamic, with a *crescendo* in the final bars. This to me suggests the answering call from the opposite mountainside, much further away, so lower in volume. That said, the difference between *mf* and *mp* is not so large, so listen to ensure that *mp* still has substance and that *mf* does not shout! Whether or not you play this as an exam piece, it will be great fun to learn and perform.

Crosland	Hand in Hand	page 11

This twelve- (plus one) bar blues will be popular with examiners, taking very little time to perform at the tempo suggested. Probably also popular with students and teachers – the former because of its easily accessible style, and the latter because of the opportunity it affords to talk about and play around with the 12-bar blues: I, I, I, I, IV, IV, I, I, V, IV, I, I.

Some details worth noting about the bass. The first LH gesture moves forward to the B♭, while the second resolves to the C. Crosland only marks a definite *crescendo* the third time this happens, but it is implicit in the harmonic progressions earlier, just shouldn't be so marked. Another thing to take care over is the length of the final notes of each gesture. I find it very easy to move my concentration to the other hand, and forget that I need to release after one crotchet – so listen out for that throughout the piece. In the RH the release at the end of the first slur will enable the *tenuto*, the slight stress, on the next note. The last chord is not so easy: make a good *rallentando* so that you have time to have all four fingers on the final notes before your arm helps to play them.

Arnold	Across the Plains	Queen's Temple

The title suggests distance and space. A crotchet pulse of c. 88 is good, allowing details of phrasing and articulation to be incorporated and registered by the listener. Two things to note: firstly there is a misprint in bar 17; the LH should play in unison with the RH, so its first note should be an E. Secondly there is a long slur over the final four bars; do not mistake this for a tie – the last Bs should be sounded with *piano* accents.

Listen for the fading of the sound on the pauses at the opening. The first two notes are confident, summoning. Then wait until the B has faded to a good *piano*, before the distant echo responds. Again, wait until the atmosphere of the introduction has dispelled before entering firmly with the main theme. Small details, but learning listening skills is essential and this will also create a time-suspended atmosphere. Unslurred crotchets need definition and should not be linked to the next notes (eg from bars 11 to 12 or 14 to 15). The canon effect from bar

7 will need careful practice, and note the stark contrasts in dynamics – playing scales at *f* or *p* levels will help, always connecting dynamic to mood: confident vs diffident; certain vs hesitant; bright vs subdued. Perhaps here the effect should be one of near vs far.

Crosland	Can't Stop Myself	Spartan

This jazzy piece is based on a twelve-bar blues and shouldn't take too long to learn, with its repetition of motifs and general catchiness. 'Swing the quavers' Crosland instructs. We don't do it as well as the real jazz pianists, but play the quavers as the last of a group of triplets, and that will work very well. Notice the D♯ in bar 9 and the E♭ two bars later. A useful point of theory to talk about there. The accented notes and chords in bars 10 & 12 are not *staccato*, so give these length as well as extra energy. How will you play the *sf* accented chords in those bars differently from the *sf tenuto* at the end? Maybe the latter has more weight behind the sound, whereas the former use strength to get the accent?

The marked tempo is pretty fast, and something a little less speedy, perhaps around 138, would also be acceptable. No repeat in the exam...and no singing either!

Diabelli	Bagatelle	Kjos

Not every young pianist will be ready for the three-note chords in this piece, but it's a reliable choice otherwise, with the simple, classical harmonies that every pianist needs to have under their fingers. No repeats necessary in the exam, and a tempo of around 112 crotchets per minute works well.

The mood is contented rather than jolly and gently separated chords in the bass will help this, while the RH sings its melody *cantabile*. Watch how a supple wrist will naturally adjust as you cover the octave in the opening arpeggio. As soon as you play the second crotchet, the G, the thumb releases the D, and releases any tension too, quickly returning to its usual position beside the second finger. Similarly, once you reach the top D, let the hand find its natural five-finger position, using a 3 to play the B, and then stretching down to the E in the next bar. Do discuss the primary triad harmonies and find the same chords in other keys. I would begin work on the three note chords by playing the outside notes first, watching the thumb change position, then play the top third, using 3 only on the F♯. Pianists should quickly learn these from memory, hearing how each chord fits under the notes of the melody, and noticing how the F♯ is only needed in the chord when the melody doesn't include it in its own part.

Emonts	Tango	Schott

That bass line, the first four notes of the descending melodic minor, has been used in countless pieces, yet remains irresistible. It circles around, each time ending on the dominant, so needing to return to the start yet again. The final two bars find a resolution of sorts, although a little abruptly perhaps, but this motif suits the dark, slightly dangerous, twilit world of the tango.

You will want to find a comfortable fingering for the LH thirds – that suggested may not suit all hands. The goal is perfect synchronisation, which means that both fingers want to be resting on the keys before the arm helps to depress them. 1 & 3 are good, but 2 & 4 are ideal as the hand is so well balanced around the middle finger; perhaps try 1/3, 2/4, 1/3, 2/4? The footwork in a tango is often complicated and has to be very precise to avoid kicked shins! One element of that precision needed here is in the rests. Two beats only on the RH note in bar 2; the cutting off of the note, just at the beginning of the third beat, should be obvious in this *f* dynamic and adds an edge to the mood. A small *diminuendo* in bars 6-8 sounds natural and makes sense of the *f* in bar 9. The sudden *pp* is another disturbing moment for the audience. Make it as soft as you can, but always with the melody projecting a little above the accompaniment. The last surprise comes with the final 'olé', as a perfectly controlled drop/float technique helps the final resolution disappear into silence...

Goedicke   Dance   *Trinity*

A strong rhythmic pulse and careful grading of dynamic levels are necessary for a successful performance of this playful dance. Play the *staccato* notes crisply and the quavers evenly, holding the minims for their full value. Ensure that chords are places firmly and listen for all notes sounding together.

This 16-bar piece in E minor has four phrases; the first one repeated three times but with two differences. Notice that the RH in bar 8 is a slightly decorated version of bar 4, and that the last phrase (starting in bar 13) is *f* (instead of *mf*). The third phrase (from bar 9) starts *p* – as you build the *crescendo* see if you can do so gradually rather than all at once.

Graupner   Bourrée   *Breitkopf*

That opening stretch of a minor sixth immediately sets the mood – one that to my mind doesn't quite go with a teddy bear baking a cake for a crocodile! It is one of the most expressive intervals, and the ensuing descent of the line makes the opening hopefulness of the sixth even more touching. This is both stylistically sophisticated and musically satisfying.

A tempo of ♩ = 69 will balance the movement of a dance with the plaintive nature of the melody. The slurs emphasise dissonances and emotive intervals, but also imply that unslurred crotchets should be articulated. No need to play them *staccato*, a small detachment from neighbouring notes is enough, and quavers can be played *legato*. This is typically what we often do in baroque music. The bigger intervals in the bass should also be articulated, for instance in bars 3 & 4. When practising the dynamic contrasts, be sure to do them in both hands, not just the RH. No need for repeats in the exam.

Moss
arr. Wedgwood   The Floral Dance (duet)   *Faber*

This wonderfully cheeky duet, with memories of the inimitable Terry Wogan, begins innocently enough but firstly migrates up a tone, then suddenly changes style as a jazz band takes over the final phrases. Enormous fun, but notice that the melodic material is not all in the primo, so it is useful to teach pianists to sing in the missing bars so that the melody sounds complete.

Some articulation is written in, but that leaves us wondering what to do in other places. For instance, bars 7 & 8: you have to separate the repeated notes, but what about the other crotchets, or the quavers? Well, the answer is that the secondo part plays this material first in the preceding bars, so whatever they do, primo must copy. There's no right answer here, but good chamber music means listening to your partner and responding to what they do. The indication 'more relaxed' and the change to a jazzy style implies using a swung rhythm (as triplets) instead of a tight dotted rhythm as notated. Swing the quaver C in bar 36 too. The notes are relatively simple, but listen to match the sound as the hands pass the themes between them. We shouldn't be able to tell when the right is playing, or when the left, they should blend into one melodic line. Ingenious and great fun to perform.

Rybicki   In the Boat   *Breitkopf*

This is a genuinely touching piece; tinges of F minor add sophistication to the harmonic language, while the melodic material is simple, based largely on one motif, which is inverted in the third line. Very skilfully done and a joy to work on.

Although feeling one in a bar will help create longer lines, it is necessary to express the metronome mark in quavers – around 104 quavers a minute. I'm sure all teachers will encourage pianists to learn the LH as chords to begin with, making sure that they are understood as part of the key, not learnt in isolation. What does the A♭ add to bar 2? If you play an A♮ instead, how does it sound and feel? Why is bar 7 slightly different in the LH from bar 3? Play them the other way round and see how they work with the RH melody. We usually remember what we understand, so discovering the reasons behind what works and

what doesn't is important, and will make the next piece using similar harmonies easier to learn. Check that the wrist is free to help find a flowing *cantabile* for the melody and perhaps use the same fingering each time for the same figuration, ie starting on a 4 at the beginning too. One to savour – they don't make so many like this!

Telemann   Minuet   *Kjos*

Telemann deserves a prize for having had a piece in the Grade 1 syllabus for at least the last ten years. This is perhaps not the most imaginative, basically staying with tonic/dominant harmonies throughout, but it has some useful teaching features. Minuets are elegant dances and a tempo of around ♩ = 104 is definitely fast enough when you are manoeuvring around the dance floor in a long, wide skirt. The pulse needs to be stable, unhurried, but buoyant, with a sense of greater lightness on the second and third beats of the bar. Fitting triplets then duplets into the beat will probably not be a problem, but using words is always helpful: 'see how the butterfly lands on the rose' would fit bars 9 & 10 perfectly. Lastly the dynamic contrasts in the second section. Perhaps one group of dancers leads the way, then another smaller, shyer group copies? Perhaps the whole band play the *f* bars, then a quartet only play the *p* echoes.

Terzibaschitsch   The First Day at School   *Trinity*

This cheerful piece is not an easy option and you may need some strategies in place to help the LH learn all the chords. One suggestion would be not to worry at first about the actual notes, but to get used to recognising the size of the interval, both by looking at it on the page, and identifying it aurally too. Then practise playing all the intervals – everything from a second to an octave is used here – with the same bottom note, or the same top note, listening carefully to the character of each one and feeling their size under the hand. Can you find a sixth, or an octave, or a fifth without looking at the keyboard? Then, when you have thoroughly prepared the ground, you'll need to learn the specific chords here – four bars at a time, always trying to hear, sing or play the melody on top so that the chords relate to something.

Probably this is one that is better for larger hands; as well as an octave in the bass, the RH also has some wider intervals to negotiate. But it is an excellent opportunity to become comfortable with small chords and to move easily around the keyboard. I would suggest playing the RH generally *legato*, except for the repeated notes of course, allowing a small lift every four bars before the upbeat to the next phrase. ♩ = 120 is a good tempo.

Terzibaschitsch   The Last Waltz (duet)   *Trinity*

A bitter-sweet sadness pervades this attractive and, it must be said, relatively easy choice. The theme is shared between the hands – careful listening should ensure no bumps as they change over, especially on the thumbs – and is heard three times, with only minor adjustments. The test here will be creating a beautiful *cantabile* tone, in *p* at the start, but also in *f* later on. Dynamics should always be relative to mood, and there is no anger or aggression here. The melody moves to the secondo in the middle section and although both parts are marked *mf*, it is the melody we want to hear, so balance the two parts accordingly. Ensemble should be straightforward once everything has started, but playing those first notes together is often a challenge, even for the most experienced. Yes, one person may be leading, but I find that breathing together is always most successful, having that sense of pulse in the body before you begin. There is an interrupted cadence in bars 31–32 to which the primo player should also react.

Terzibaschitsch suggests *con Ped* in the secondo; it's not completely necessary, but if do you use it, make sure the melody is not too blurred, and probably avoid it altogether in the C major section. Discreet pedalling can definitely add to the nostalgic mood, but change frequently. Waltzes should usually feel one-in-a-bar: ♩. = 36 suits this piece.

Trad.
arr. Farrington   English Country Garden   *Boosey*

A memorable tune, collected by Cecil Sharp, and used, we read here, by Morris dancers as one of their Handkerchief Dances. The marked tempo is good; no faster, otherwise it will be difficult to keep the integrity of the dotted rhythm. It needs to be precise to catch the perkiness of the mood. Keep listening to ensure pianists don't slip into an easy-going triplet rhythm.

While the rhythms should be precise, the *staccato* could perhaps be more relaxed. The mood is lively – a sunny Sunday afternoon outing with the children perhaps, and if the *staccato* sounds too crisp, the whole piece takes on a military tinge. As this is an arrangement, dynamics have been left deliberately vague, so this is an opportunity to add some in yourself, keeping its relative folk simplicity in mind. An obvious example would be to play the second line at a different level, and perhaps add either a *diminuendo* or *crescendo* at the very end. Place the final chord with confidence, as the Morris men finish the dance and bow to the audience.

Teaching notes written by Pamela Lidiard

Key

A solid line denotes a piece within this book.

A dotted line denotes a piece from the alternative list.

Come Away With Me

Words & Music by Norah Jones

3. And I _____ want to walk with you _____ on a cloud-
7. And I _____ want to wake up _____ with the rain fall - ing

- y day in fields ____ where the yel - low grass grows ___ knee ___
on a tin roof while I'm ____ safe ____ there ___ in ____ your ___

To Coda ⊕

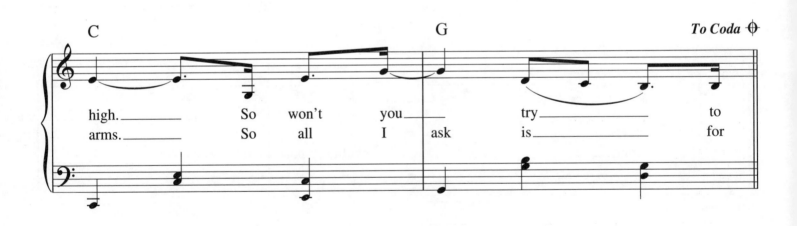

high. _____ So won't you ___ try _____ to
arms. _____ So all I ask is _____ for

come. 4. Come a - way with me ___ and ___ we'll kiss on a

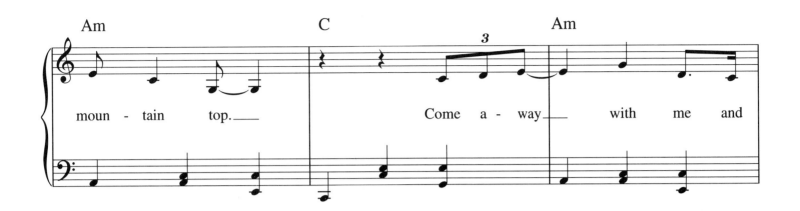

mountain top.___ Come a - way___ with me and

D.C. al Coda
(with repeat)

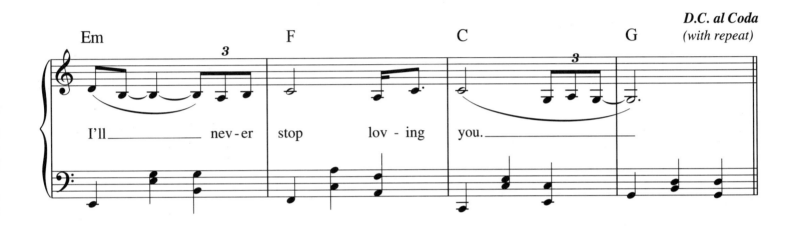

I'll___ nev-er stop lov - ing you.___

⊕ *Coda*

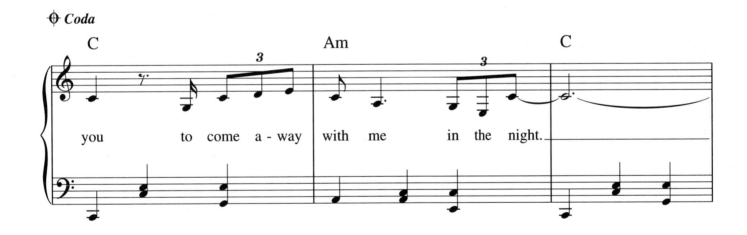

you to come a - way with me in the night.___

___ Come a - way___ with me.

15

Shoot The Moon

Words & Music by Jesse Harris

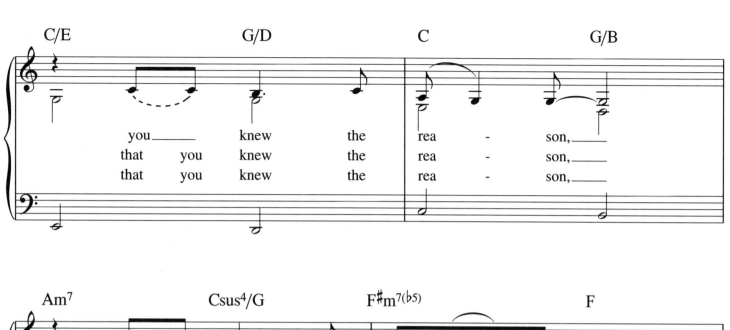

you_____ knew the rea - son,_____
that you knew the rea - son,_____
that you knew the rea - son,_____

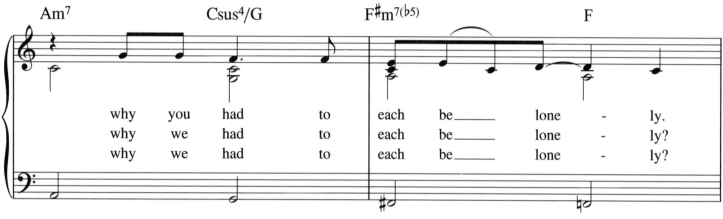

why you had to each be_____ lone - ly.
why we had to each be_____ lone - ly?
why we had to each be_____ lone - ly?

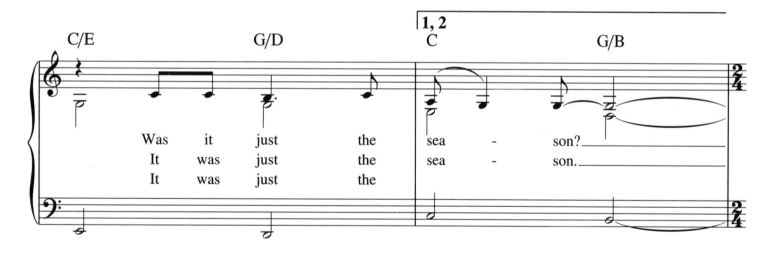

1, 2

Was it just the sea - son?_____
It was just the sea - son._____
It was just the

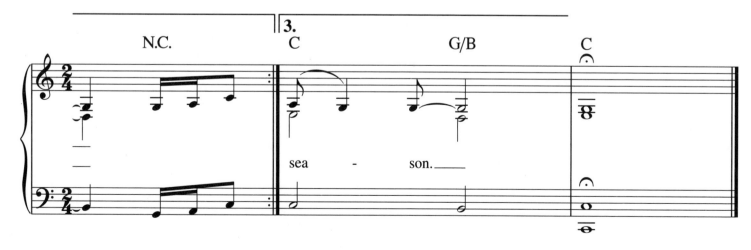

3.

sea - son._____

Turn Me On

Words & Music by John D. Loudermilk

de - sert_____ wait - ing for the rain,_____

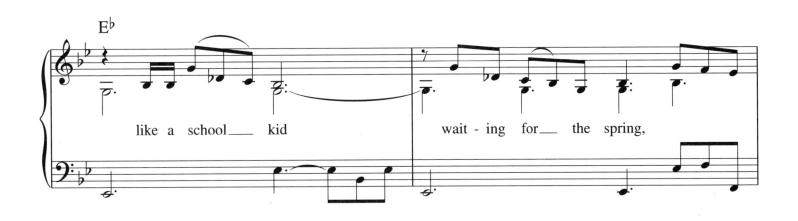

like a school___ kid wait - ing for___ the spring,

I'm just sit - ting here___ wait - ing for you to come on home and___

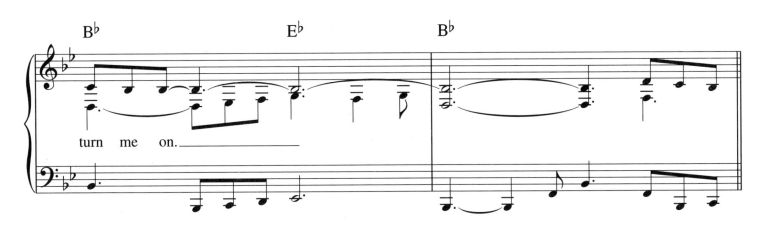

turn me on._____

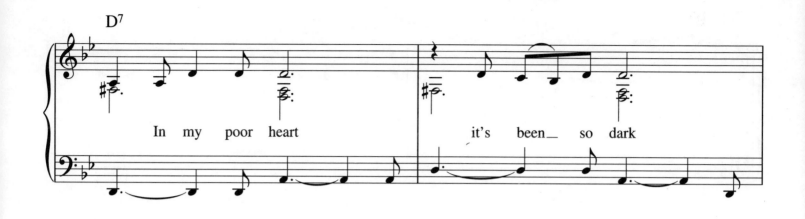

In my poor heart it's been__ so dark

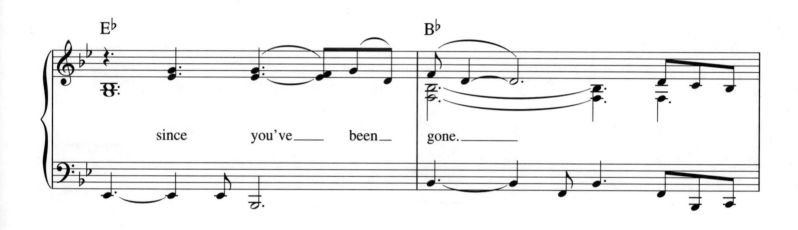

since you've____ been__ gone.____

Af - ter all,__ you're the one____ who__ turns me off;__

but you're the on - ly one_____ who can turn____ me back on.__

My hot fire's a-wait-ing for a new tube,

my glass is wait-ing for some fresh ice-cubes.

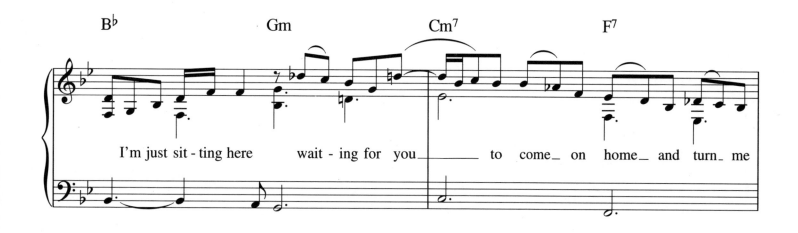

I'm just sit-ting here wait-ing for you to come on home and turn me

on, turn me on.

Lonestar

Words & Music by Lee Alexander

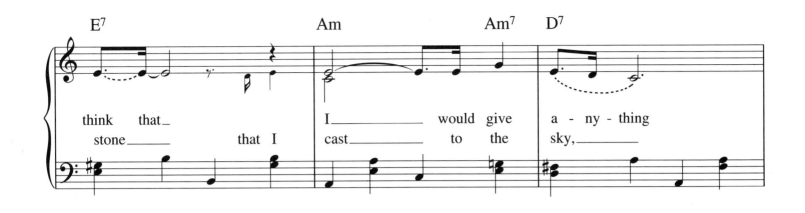

think   that   I   would   give   a - ny - thing
stone   that I   cast   to   the   sky,

1-3.

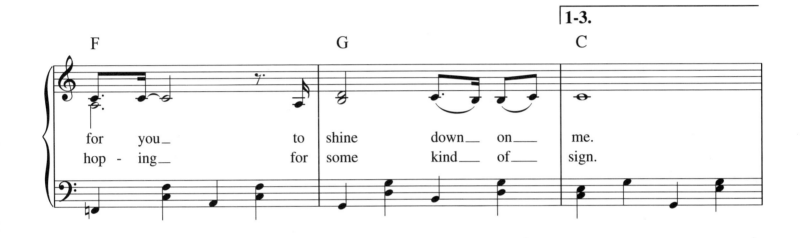

for   you   to   shine   down   on   me.
hop - ing   for   some   kind   of   sign.

4.

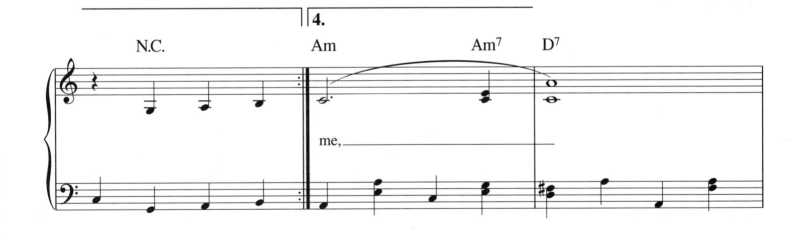

me,

rit.

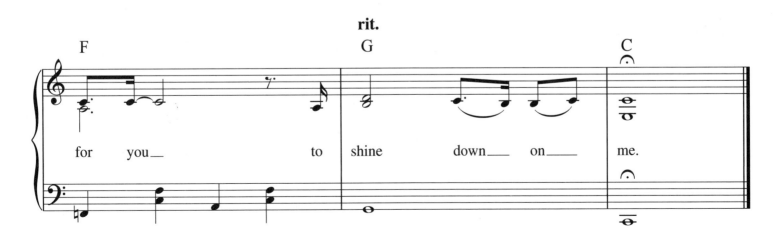

for   you   to   shine   down   on   me.

Painter Song

Words & Music by Lee Alexander & J.C. Hopkins

25

I've Got To See You Again

Words & Music by Jesse Harris

⊕ *Coda*

- gain._____ Oh,___ I can't

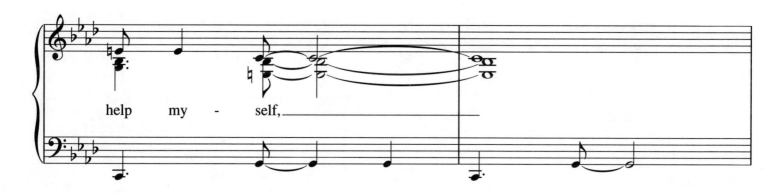

help my - self,_____

I've got to see__ you__ a - gain._____

Verse 3:
But no, I won't go for any of those things
To not touch your skin is not why I sing,
I can't help myself
I've got to see you again.

Verse 4:
Instrumental

Verse 5:
No, I won't go to share you with them
But oh, even though I know where you've been,
I can't help myself
I've got to see you again.

One Flight Down

Words & Music by Jesse Harris

Nightingale

Words & Music by Norah Jones

34

The Long Day Is Over

Words & Music by Norah Jones & Jesse Harris

The Nearness Of You

Words by Ned Washington
Music by Hoagy Carmichael

Freely ♩ = c. 56

It's not the pale moon that ex - cites me, that

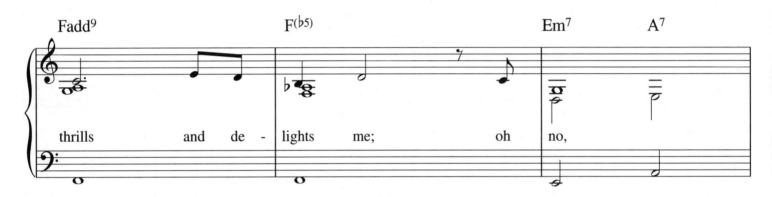

thrills and de - lights me; oh no,

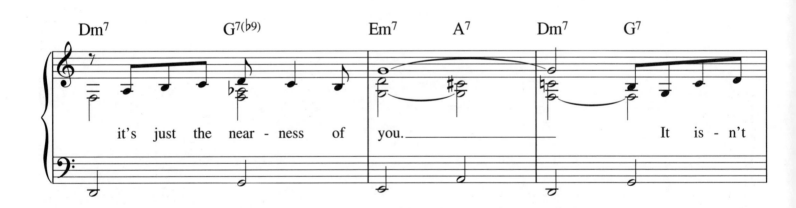

it's just the near - ness of you. It is - n't

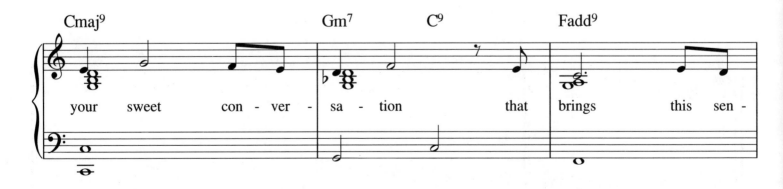

your sweet con - ver - sa - tion that brings this sen -

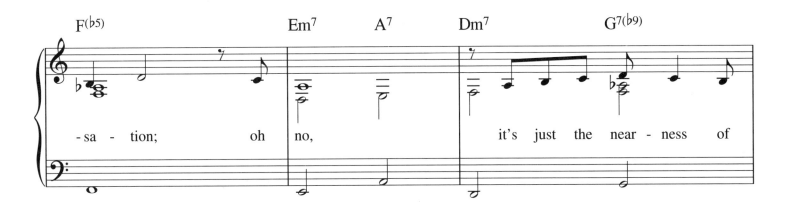

-sa - tion; oh no, it's just the near - ness of

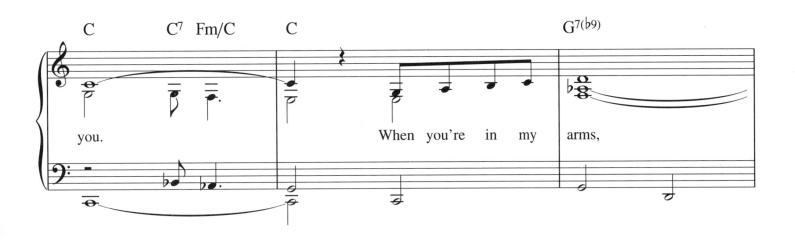

you. When you're in my arms,

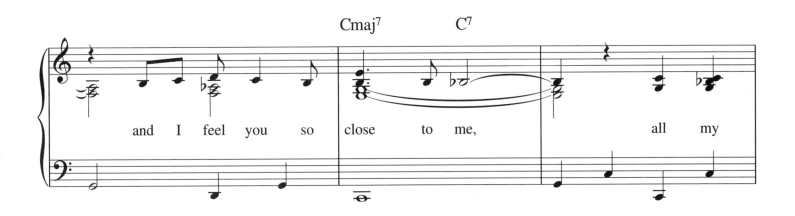

and I feel you so close to me, all my

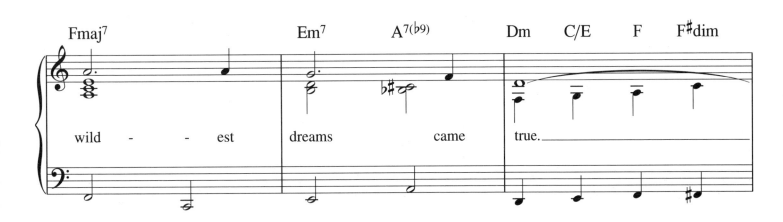

wild - - est dreams came true._____

make this end - less day end - less night_____

to - night!_____

7

To - day the world was just an

a tempo

N.C.

70

night._____

marc.

73

CARRICKFERGUS

Traditional, arranged by Keith Thomas

boat - man _____ to fer - ry me ov - er, _____

my love and I. _____

To be to-

- geth-er, _____ my _____ love _____ and I. _____

Verse 2:

I wish I was in the land of Eire,
Where the mountains reach the sea,
Where flowers blossom, as I do remember,
Where my true love came to me.
But the sea is wide, and I cannot swim over,
Nor have I the wings to fly.
Ah, to be back now in Carrickfergus;
To be together, my love and I.

Habañera

Music by Georges Bizet
Words by Henry Meilhac & Ludovic Halévy after Merimée
Arranged by Jesse Cook

∞

fait, men - ace ou pri - ère, l'un par - le bien___ l'au - tre se tait; et c'est

l'au - tre que je pré - fère il n'a rien dit;___ mais il me plaît.___

L'a - mour!___ L'a - mour!___

L'a - mour!___ L'a - mour! L'a - mour est

en - fant de Bo - hême, il n'a ja - mais, ja - mais con - nu de loi; si tu ne

m'ai - me pas, je t'ai - me si je t'ai - me, prend garde à toi!_____

Si tu ne m'ai - me pas, si tu ne m'ai - me pas, je t'aime!_____

Mais, si je t'ai - me, si je t'ai - me, prend garde à_____

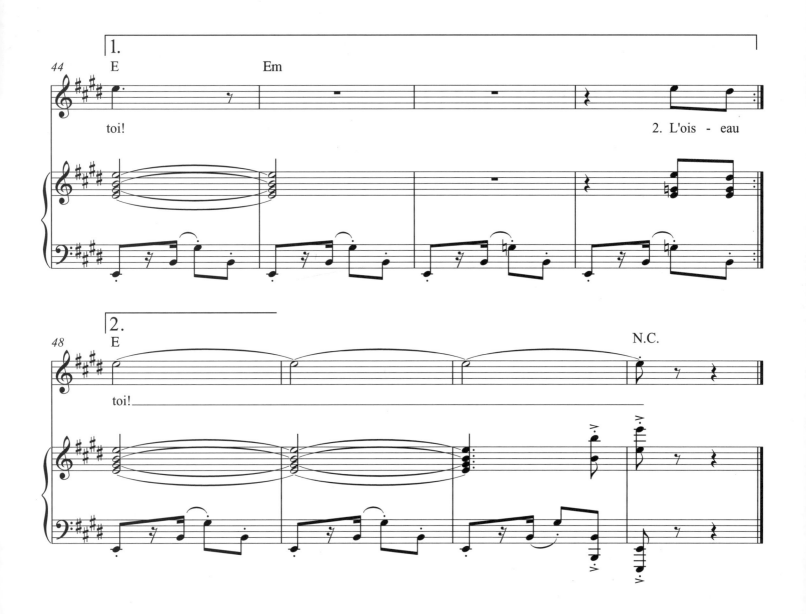

Verse 2:

L'oiseau que tu croyais surprendre
Battit de l'aile et s'envola;
L'amour est loin, tu peux l'attendre;
Tu ne l'attend plus, il est là!
Tout autour de toi vite, vite,
Il vient, s'en va, puis il revient!
Tu crois le tenir, il t'évite;
Tu crois l'éviter, il te tient!
L'amour, l'amour, l'amour, l'amour!

Bali Ha'i

Words by Oscar Hammerstein II   Music by Richard Rodgers

sea:_____ "Here am I,_____ your spe- cial is- land; come to me, come to me." Your own spe- cial hopes, your own spe- cial dreams bloom on the hill- side and shine_____ in the streams.

Papa Can You Hear Me?

Words by Alan Bergman & Marilyn Bergman
Music by Michel Legrand

oo

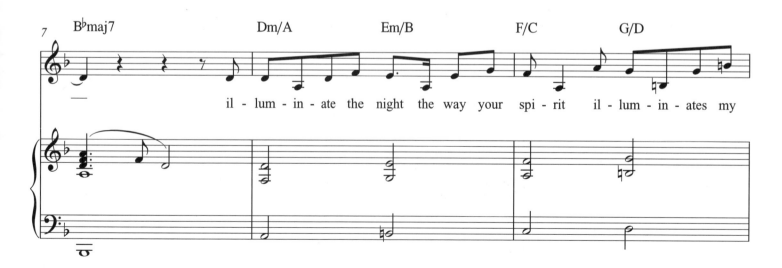

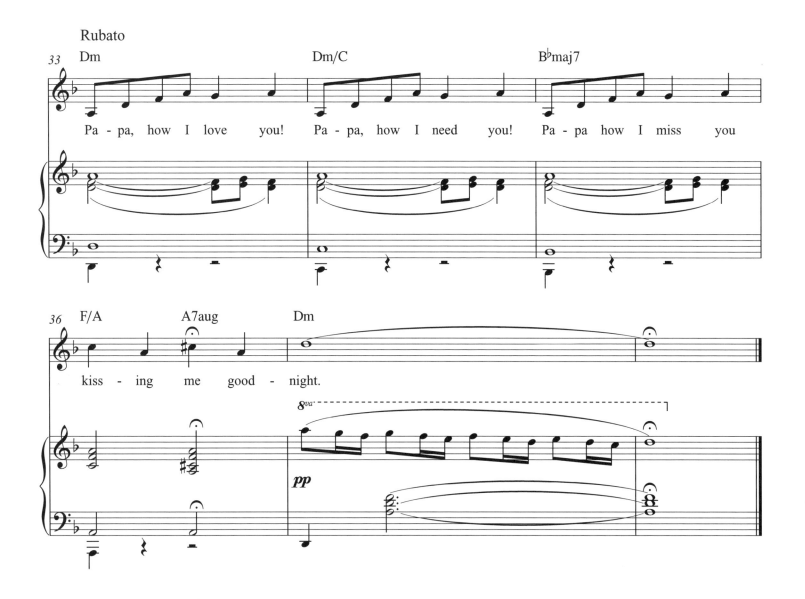

Verse 2:

Papa, please forgive me
Try to understand me
Papa, don't you know I had no choice?
Can you hear me praying?
Anything I'm saying?
Even though the night is filled with voices?
I remember everything you taught me,
Every book I've ever read.
Can all the words in all the books
Help me to face what lies ahead?
The trees are so much taller,
And I feel so much smaller,
The moon is twice as lonely
And the stars are half as bright.

The Flower Duet

By Leo Delibes   Arranged by Paul Bateman
Text by Edmond Gondinet & Philippe Gille

33

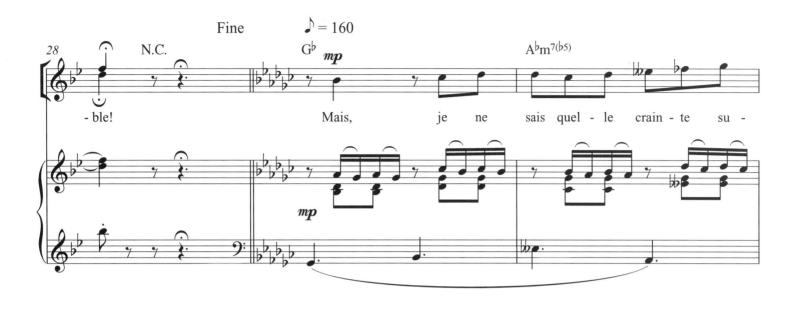

Fine   ♪ = 160

N.C.   G♭ *mp*   A♭m7(♭5)

-ble!   Mais,   je ne sais quel - le crain - te su -

mp

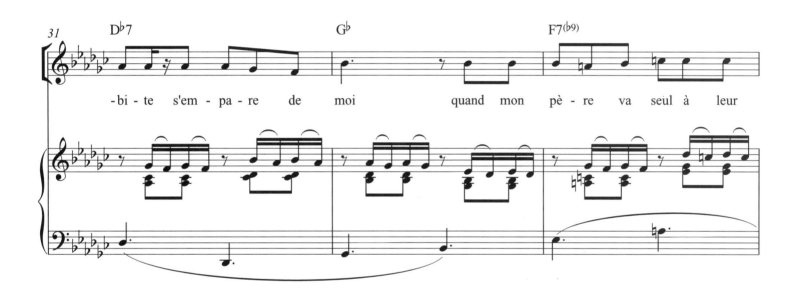

D♭7   G♭   F7(♭9)

-bi - te s'em - pa - re de moi   quand mon pè - re va seül à leur

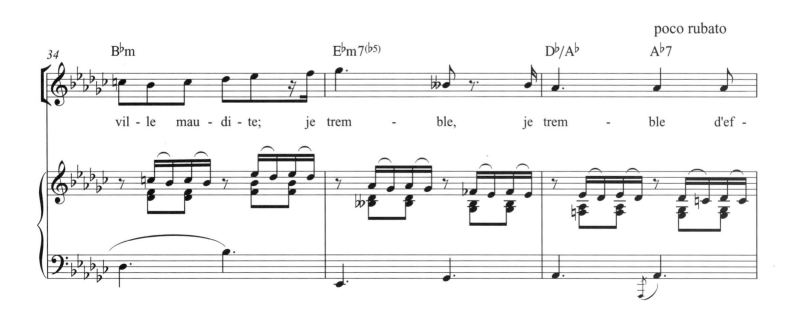

poco rubato

B♭m   E♭m7(♭5)   D♭/A♭   A♭7

vil - le mau - di - te; je trem - ble, je trem - ble d'ef -

poco rall.

37

The Water Is Wide

Traditional, arranged by Frank Gallagher

oo

Freely (♩ = c.60)

N.C.

pp

con ped.

The wat - er is wide,____ I can - not get o'er, and neith - er

have____ I wings to__ fly. Give me a__ boat____ that will car - ry____

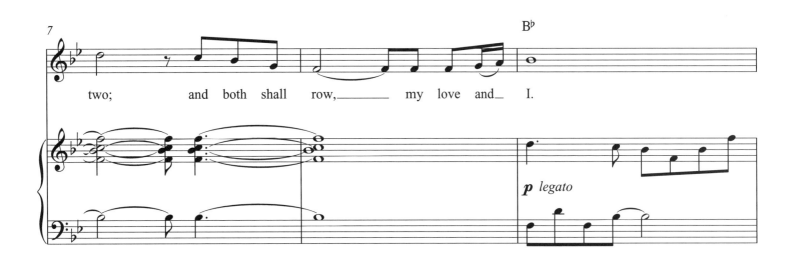

two;____ and both shall row,_____ my love and__ I.

B♭

p legato

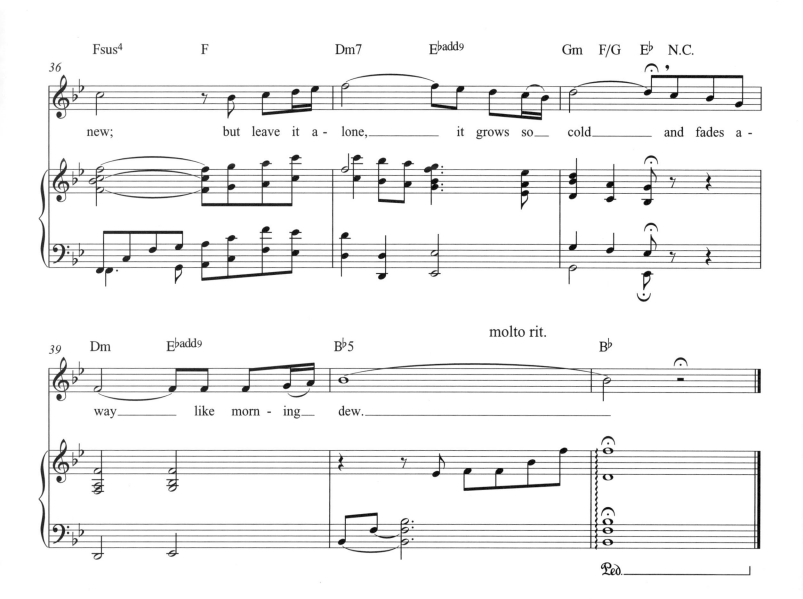

new;   but leave it a - lone,_____ it grows so_ cold_____ and fades a -

way_____ like morn - ing_ dew._____

Can't Help Lovin' Dat Man

Words by Oscar Hammerstein II   Music by Jerome Kern

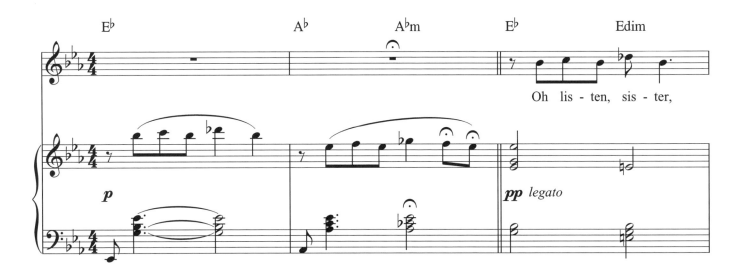

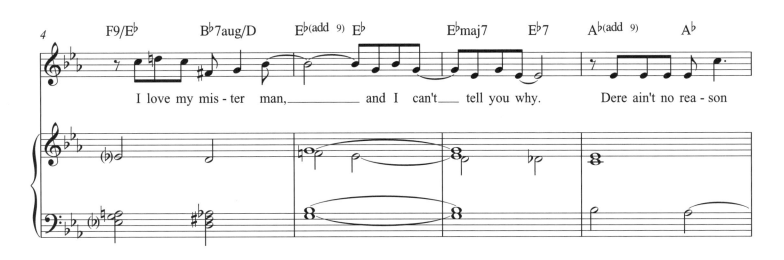

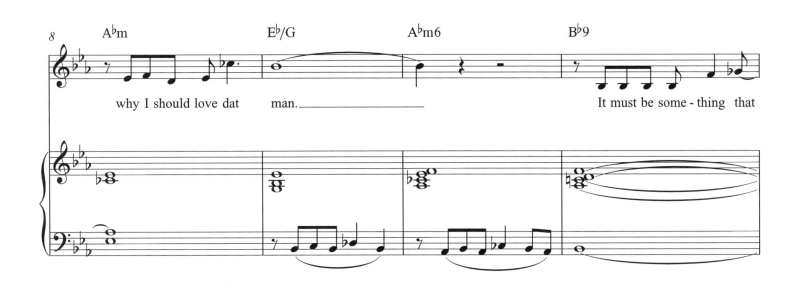

55

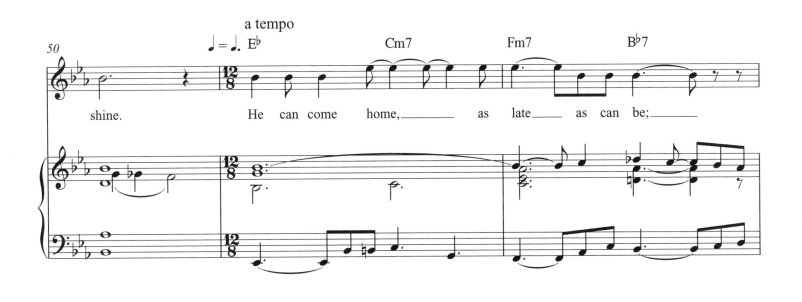

shine. He can come home,_____ as late_____ as can be;_____

to ⊕ CODA

Home with-out him_____ ain't no home to me._____ Can't help

D.S. al ⊕ CODA

lov - in'__ dat man_____ of mine._____

The Laughing Song

Composed by Johann Strauss II
Original Words by Karl Haffner & Richard Genée
English Translation by Christopher Hassall

63

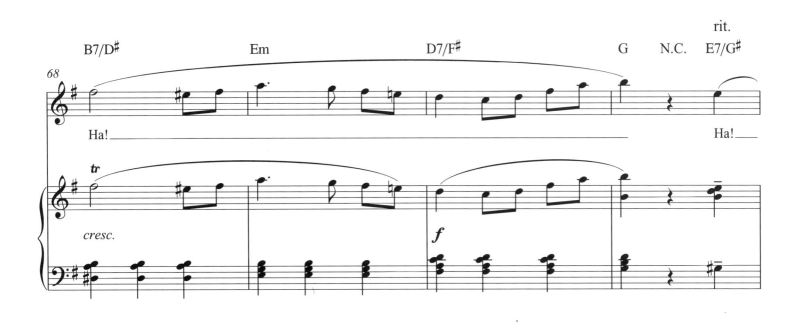

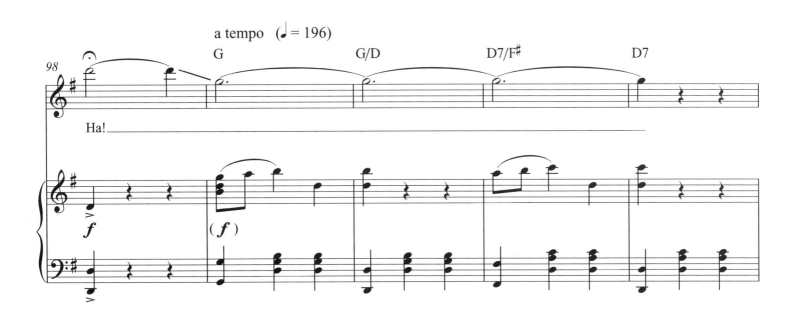

Verse 2:

Profiles, they say,
Give the game away,
When formed with classic grace.

If the head on view
Isn't much to you,
Then who can't face thine face?

What evidence more can there be? Ha ha ha ha ha.
I sing at soirées without fee, ha ha ha ha ha ha,
Bestowing my attention
With lofty condescension.
Such graces are the traces of a pedigree.
Such graces are the traces of a pedigree.

All's one to you now, I'm afraid,
Because you love a parlour maid.

What a funny, ha ha ha *etc.*

If I Loved You

Words by Oscar Hammerstein II   Music by Richard Rodgers

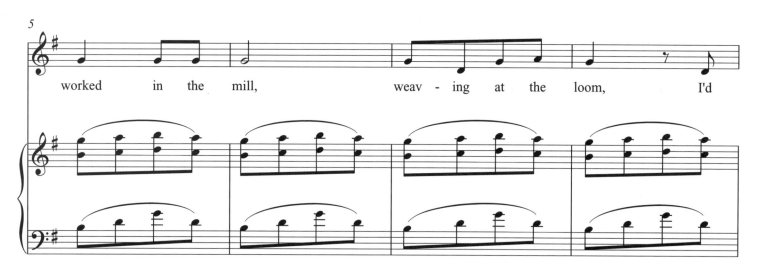

a tempo (♩ = 92)

be   If   I   loved you,

time___ and a- gain___ I would try to say all I'd

want you to know.___

più mosso

If I loved you, words___ would-n't come___ in an

A Bit Of Earth

Words by Lucy Simon   Music by Marsha Norman

oo

Freely (♩ = c.80)
N.C.

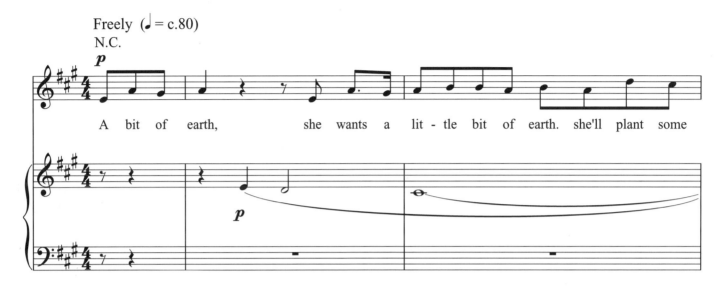

A bit of earth, she wants a lit-tle bit of earth. she'll plant some

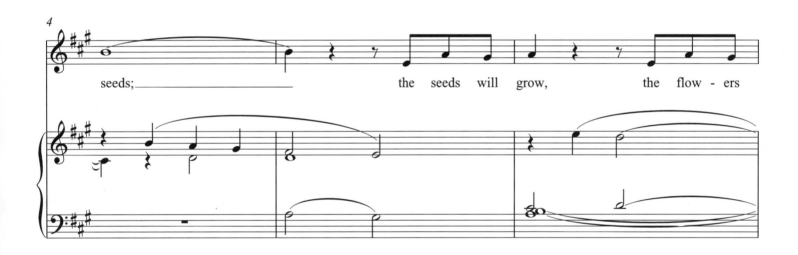

seeds;_____ the seeds will grow, the flow-ers

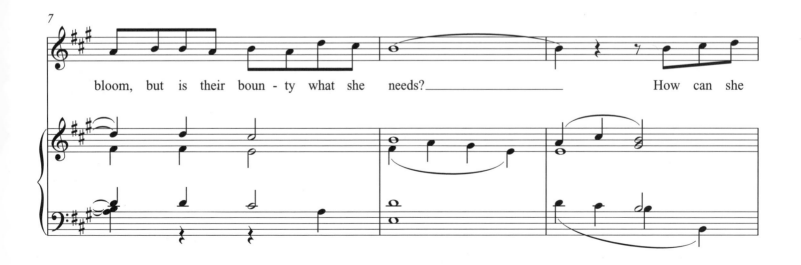

bloom, but is their boun-ty what she needs?_____ How can she

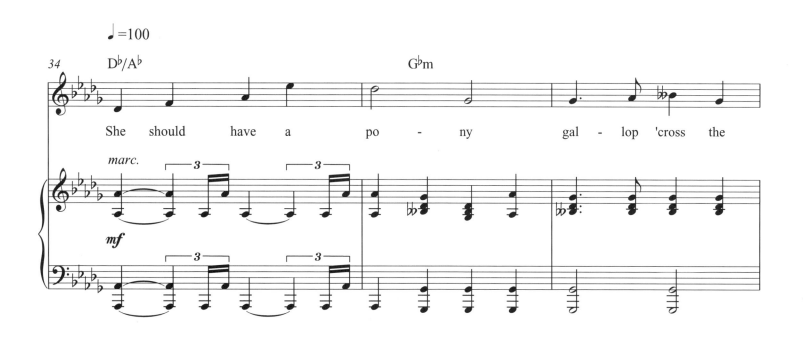

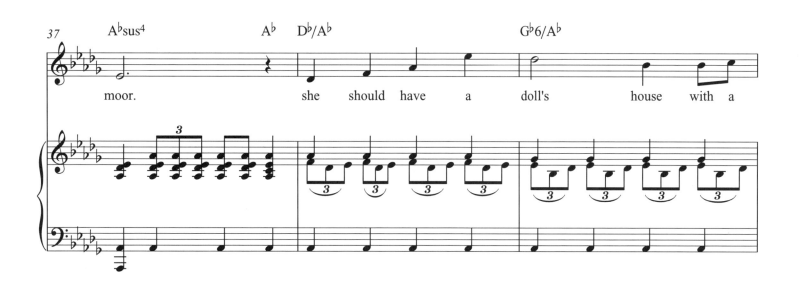

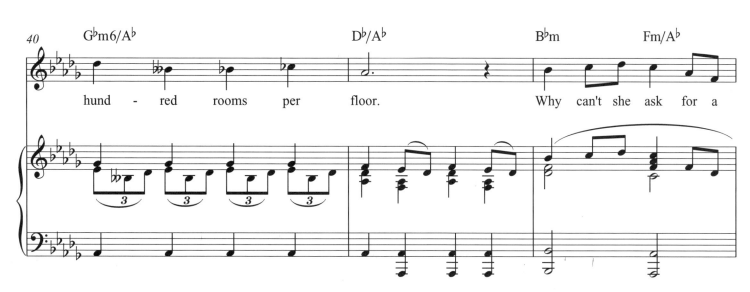

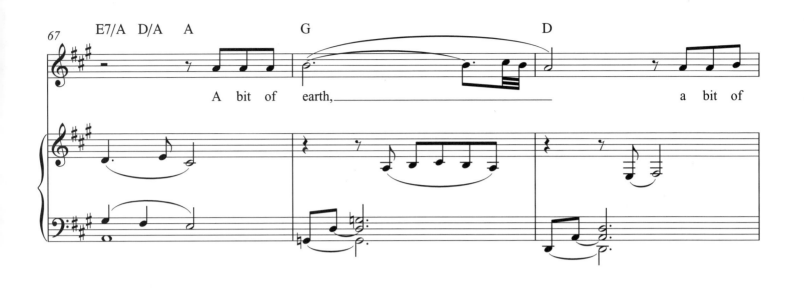

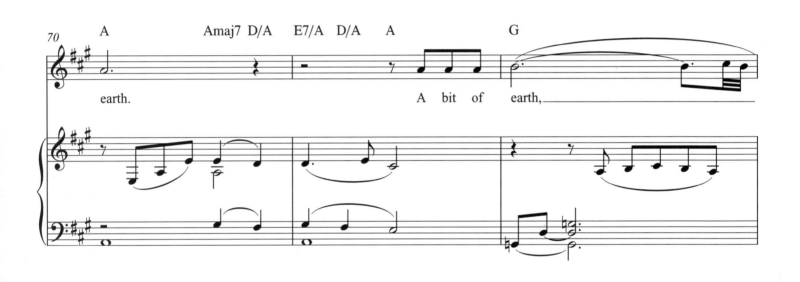

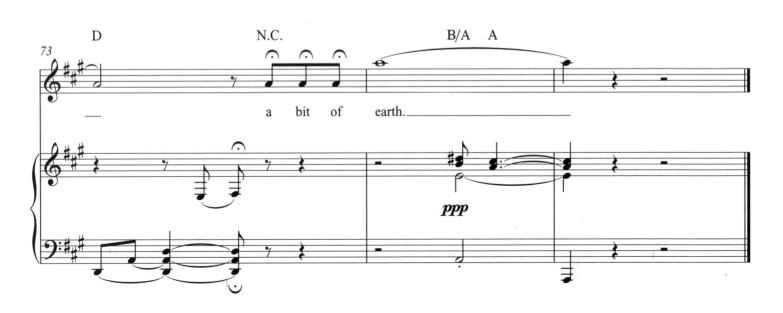

Somewhere

Words by Stephen Sondheim   Music by Leonard Bernstein

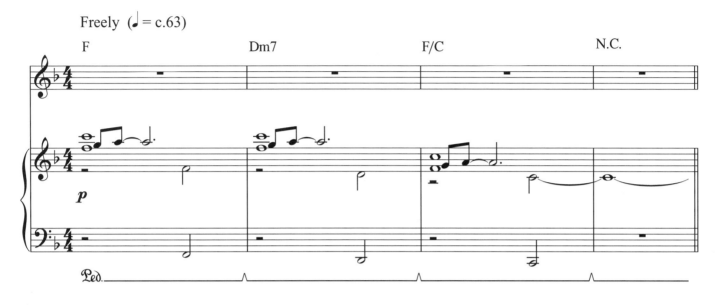

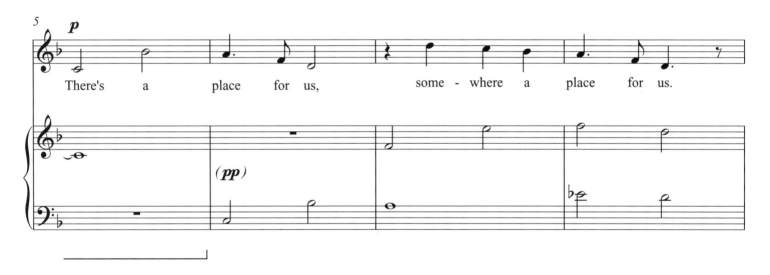

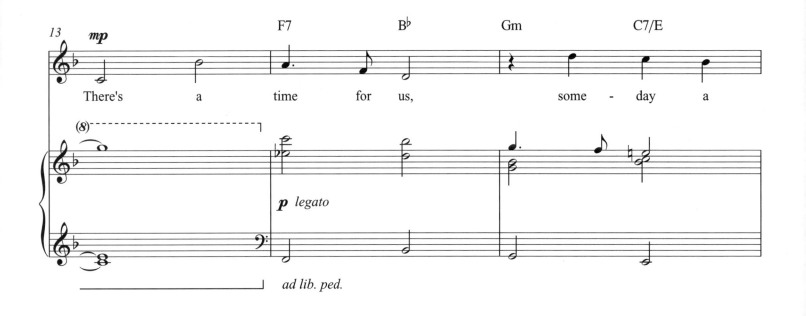

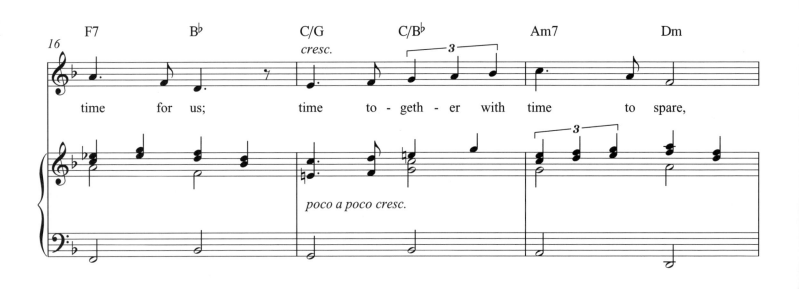

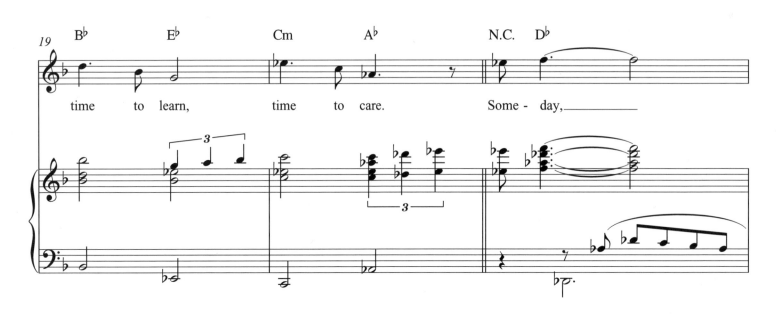

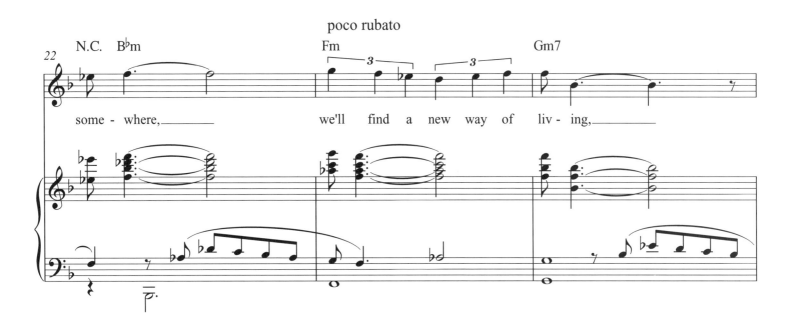

some - where,_____ we'll find a new way of liv - ing,_____

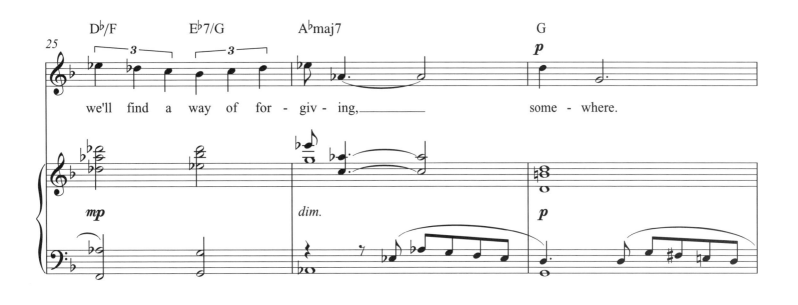

we'll find a way of for - giv - ing,_____ some - where.

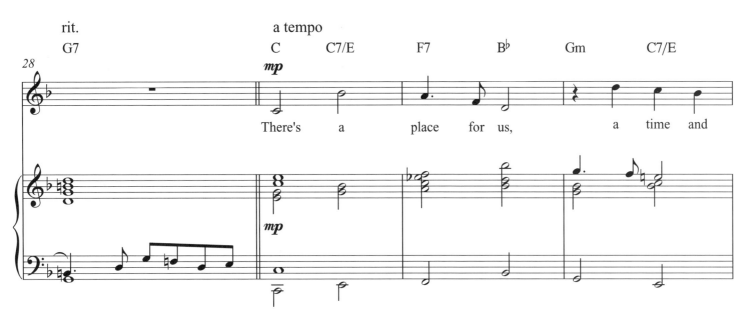

There's a place for us, a time and

place for us. Hold my hand and we're half - way there. Hold my hand and I'll

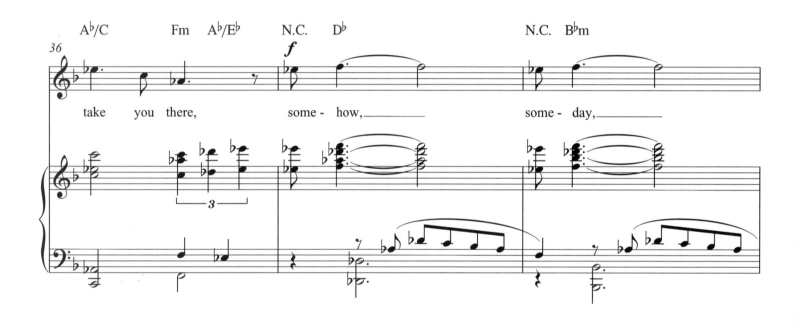

take you there, some - how,____ some - day,____

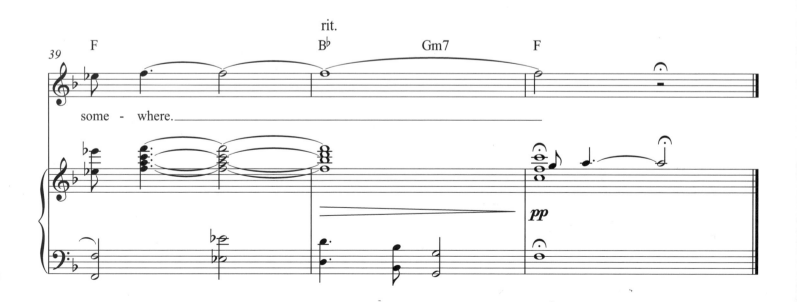

some - where._____

The Prayer

Words & Music by David Foster & Carole Bayer Sager
Italian Translation by Alberto Testa & Tony Renis

It's The Heart That Matters Most

Words & Music by Steve Mac, Wayne Hector & Don Black

2. It's still the same old   Al - ways the heart that mat - ters most.

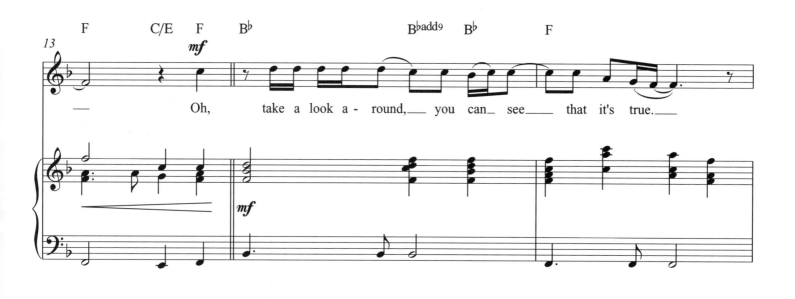

Oh,   take a look a - round,___ you can___ see___ that it's true.___

It's like a riv - er flow - ing in - side___ of you.___   Ev - 'ry - one needs love,___ you

need_ it too.___ So here's what you___ have got to___ do.___ Spread a lit-tle

hope,_____ make the spi-rits rise._____ Do you see the won - der in___ their eyes?_

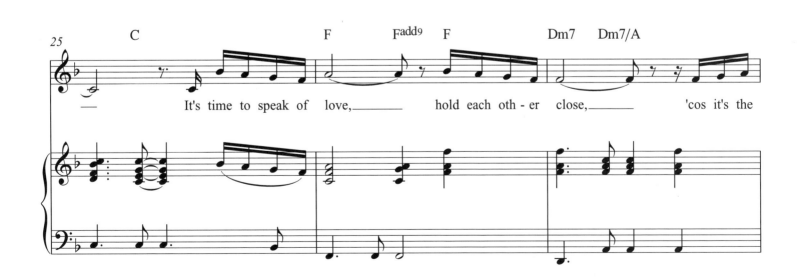

— It's time to speak of love,_____ hold each oth - er close,_____ 'cos it's the

Verse 2:

It's still the same old moon.
Why does it shine so bright?
There's a little magic in the air tonight.
Time to speak of love,
Hold each other close,
'Cos it's the heart that matters most.